One Sunday morning, the warm sun came up and Bump! - out of bed crawled a very thirsty gentleman.

He started to look for some booze.

At **10am**, he drank one bottle of champagne, but he was still thirsty.

At **11am**, he drank two pints of real ale, but he was still thirsty.

At **12am**, he drank three pints of lager, but he was still thirsty.

At **1pm**, he drank four pints of stout, but he was still thirsty.

At **2pm**, he drank five shots of tequila, but he was still thirsty.

At 3pm, he got through

one Whiskey Sour, one Gin and Tonic, one Dry Martini, one Screwdriver, one Brandy Alexander,

one delicious Manhattan, one Tom Collins, one zesty Margarita, one large Mojito, and one Black Velvet.

That afternoon, he didn't feel
very well at all.

At 6pm, he got through one nice Bloody Mary
and after that he felt much better.

Now he wasn't thirsty any more -
and he couldn't tell the time anymore.
He had one big, fat hangover.

He cocooned himself in the garden shed. He stayed inside for one whole week and swore that he would never drink again. Then he gobbled down an egg and bacon roll, had a mug of tea, pulled himself together and...

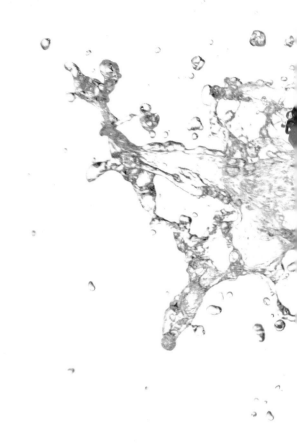

He was ready to party again!